When You Say Nothing
& 9 more great chart hits

CONTENTS

Production: Miranda Steel

Published 1999

International
MUSIC
Publications

International Music Publications Limited
Griffin House 161 Hammersmith Road London W6 8BS England

Beautiful Stranger

Words and Music by
MADONNA CICCONE and WILLIAM ORBIT

strang - er.____ Da da da da da da da da da da da da da.____

____ Beau - ti - ful strang - er.____

Repeat ad lib. and fade

Bills, Bills, Bills

Words and Music by
KANDI L BURRUSS, KEVIN BRIGGS, BEYONCE KNOWLES,
KELLY ROWLAND and LE TOYA LUKETT

Moderately, half-time feel

At first we start-ed out real cool,
Now you've been max-in' out my card,

tak-in' me plac-es I had nev-er been. But now
gave me bad cred-it, buy me gifts with my own name.

From The Heart

Words and Music by
DIANE WARREN

Doo Dah

Words by TOONIE and SPONGE
Music by TOONIE, SPONGE and SHOOTER

Ev - ery - bo - dy sing this song, doo-dah, doo-dah, well ev - ery - bo - dy sing this song

all the doo - dah day. Ev - ery - bo - dy sing this song, doo - dah, doo - dah, well

ev - ery - bo - dy sing this song all the doo - dah day,

all the doo - dah day. Ev - ery - bo - dy sing this song,

la la la la _____

all the doo-dah day.

Kiss Me

Words and Music by
MATT SLOCUM

Kiss ___ me, out of the beard - ed bar - ley ___
Kiss ___ me down by the bro - ken tree - house, ___

___ night - ly, be - side the green, green grass, ___
___ swing ___ me up - on its hang - ing tire, ___

My Love Is Your Love

Words and Music by
WYCLEF JEAN and JERRY DUPLESSIS

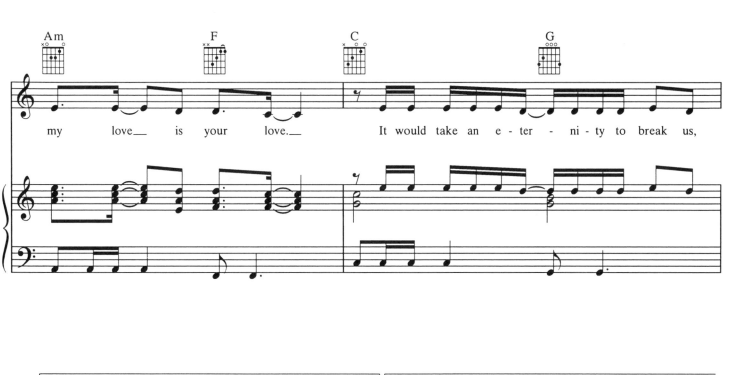

my love____ is your love.____ It would take an e - ter - ni - ty to break us,

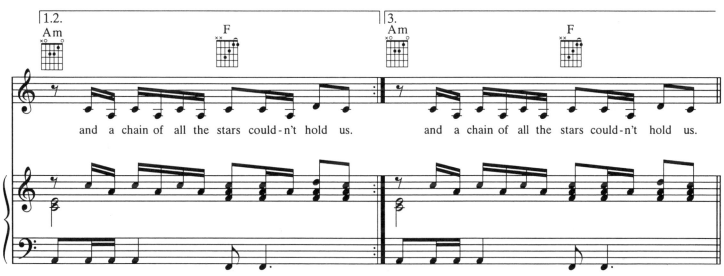

and a chain of all the stars could-n't hold us.

and a chain of all the stars could-n't hold us.

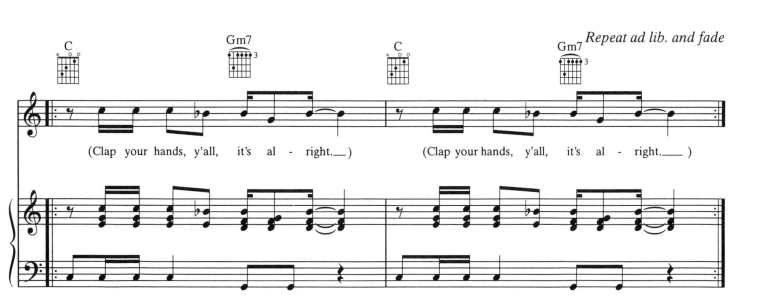

Repeat ad lib. and fade

(Clap your hands, y'all, it's al - right.___) (Clap your hands, y'all, it's al - right.___)

She

Words by CHARLES AZNAVOUR
Music by HERBERT KRETZMER

When You Say Nothing At All

Words and Music by
PAUL OVERSTREET and DON SCHLITZ

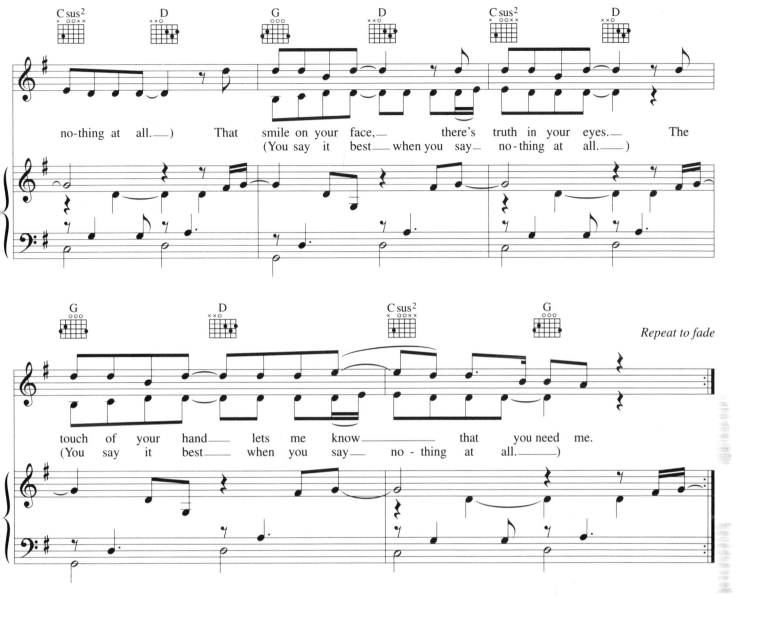

no-thing at all.__) That smile on your face,__ there's truth in your eyes.__ The
(You say it best__ when you say__ no-thing at all.__)

touch of your hand__ lets me know__ that you need me.
(You say it best__ when you say__ no-thing at all.__)

Repeat to fade

Verse 2:

All day long I can hear people talking out loud
But when you hold me you drown out the crowd
Try as they may they can never defy
What's been said between your heart and mine.

The smile on your face *etc.*

You Get What You Give

Words and Music by
GREGG ALEXANDER and RICK NOWELS

In Our Lifetime

Words and Music by
JOHN McELHONE and SHARLEEN SPITERI